THE CORN HUSK DOLL

written by Melissa Schiller

illustrated by Sandra Speidel

SCHOLASTIC INC.

New York   Toronto   London   Auckland   Sydney
Mexico City   New Delhi   Hong Kong   Buenos Aires

Developed by Kirchoff/Wohlberg, Inc., in cooperation with Scholastic Inc.

4 5 6 7 8 9 10   08   09 08 07 06 05 04

It was Sunday evening and Sue still did not have an idea for her school project. In the morning she was supposed to tell her teacher what food or craft she would be making.

"Would you please help me?" Sue asked her mother. They talk about several ideas. Then Sue made a choice. She loved Mom's idea about making corn muffins. They got out Grandma's old recipe box.

Mom said there was nothing better than the smell of freshly baked corn muffins. Then Mom had another idea.

"I thought of something," Mom said.

"Better than corn muffins?" Sue asked. "What is it?"

"Yes, just wait," Mom said and ran upstairs. She came down with an old corn husk doll.

"When I was a little girl, my grandmother and I used to make dolls out of corn husks. I'm pretty sure I can remember how it was done. It wasn't hard."

"Do you mean we can make one?" asked Sue.

"We can try," said Mom.

By the next weekend they had everything they needed to get to work. They had bought ears of corn, peeled off the husks, and dried them.

Sue helped Mom. As she worked, Mom explained what to do. Sue carefully wrote down the directions. She thought it would be fun to give the directions to children in her class. She began by listing the materials.

What You Need:

dried corn husks
straight pins
pipe cleaners
string
a pan of warm water
yarn or corn silk
a marking pen

Then Sue wrote each step:

1. Take husks off the ears of corn. Dry them for a week.

2. When you are ready to make a doll, soak the husks in a pan of warm water for about five minutes. This makes them easy to use.

3. Make the doll's head first.
• Tear off a 1/4-inch wide strip from one of the husks.
• Rip down the full length of the husk. Roll it into a ball.
• Use a straight pin to fix the ends.

4. To make the upper body:
• Take another strip of corn husk.
• Roll it into a ball.
• Fix the end with a straight pin, too.

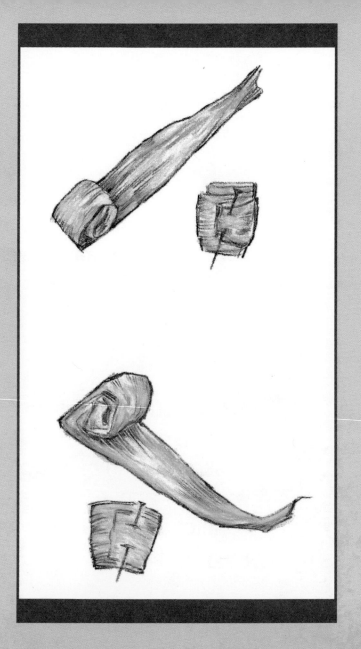

5. Take 3 pieces of corn husk, each about 1 inch wide.
• Wind them loosely around a pipe cleaner to make the arms.
• Cut off the leftover husk.
• Tie the ends with string.

6. Take a full-length strip of husk about 1 inch wide.
• Drape it over the head from front to back.

7. Take a piece of string. Use the string to tie the husk around just under the head.
• Tie it tightly to make the doll's neck.
• The husk below the string can be trimmed later.

8. Slip the arms you have already made under the neck piece. While you hold this, put the upper body under the arms. The upper body will hold the arms in place.

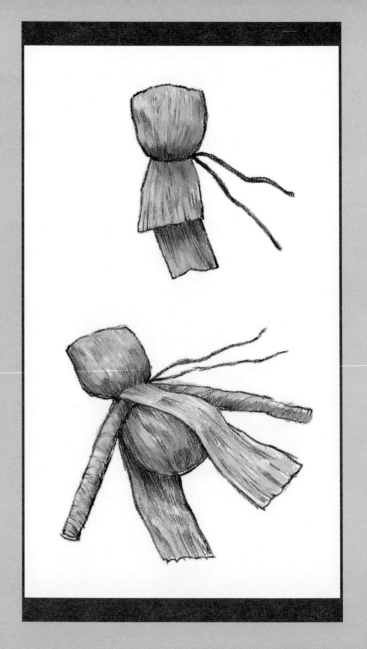

9. Wrap the last parts of the long strip of husk around the upper body. This should hold it in place.
• Tie with string. This makes the doll's waist.

10. To make a skirt, take a long strip of husk.
• Place the center of the husk on the waistline.
• Tie this strip at the waist with string.
• Let the top ends fall down over the string.
• Continue to add as many husks as you like to make a full skirt.

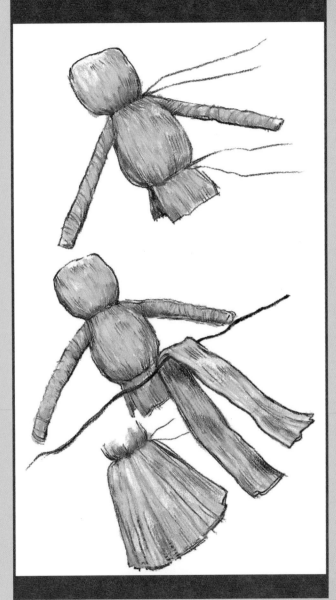

11. To make hair, take some yellow corn silk or yarn.
• Glue several strands at a time to the head of the doll.

12. To paint the face, use a black felt tip pen to draw your doll's face.

Sue loved her finished doll. She placed it on the table right next to her mother's doll.

Sue decided to learn more about corn husk dolls. She and her mom went to their computer. They looked on the Internet to find information about corn husk dolls.

They saw pictures of some wonderful dolls made long ago. They found out that many people still enjoy the craft of making corn husk dolls.

Sue took her doll and her mother's doll to school the next day. She showed her doll first and explained that she and her mother had made it together. She showed the other doll and explained that it had been made years ago by her mother and her mother's grandmother.

Sue gave a copy of the directions for making the doll to each of her classmates. She hoped one or two of them would like to make one.

No one in the class had ever heard of a corn husk doll. Sue explained that Native American people had made dolls like these. Children who lived in the first colonies played with corn husk dolls. So did children who moved west in covered-wagon trains.

Later that day, two of Sue's friends asked if she would help them each make a corn husk doll.

The next weekend the three children met at Sue's house. They were ready to make the corn husk dolls. Sue had gotten together everything they would need. She had plenty of dried corn husks left over. They each brought their copy of the directions.

Sue read the directions aloud. She helped her friends follow the directions, step by step.

   While they worked, the friends talked about why children long ago in America made corn husk dolls. They talked about the fact that there were no huge toy stores like there are today. They wondered if they would have liked living in a time with no toy stores.

   They worked side by side. By the end of the afternoon, they each had made a wonderful corn husk doll.